BLOOD CROWN QUEST
SANDS OF BLOOD

Steve Barlow and Steve Skidmore
Illustrated by Jack Lawrence

First published in 2013
by Franklin Watts

Text © Steve Barlow and Steve Skidmore 2013
Illustrations by Jack Lawrence © Franklin Watts 2013
Cover design by Jonathan Hair
The "2Steves" illustrations by Paul Davidson
used by kind permission of Orchard Books

Franklin Watts
338 Euston Road
London NW1 3BH

Franklin Watts Australia
Level 17/207 Kent Street
Sydney, NSW 2000

A CIP catalogue record for this book
is available from the British Library.

ISBN: 978 1 4451 1499 6

1 3 5 7 9 10 8 6 4 2

Printed in Great Britain

Franklin Watts is a division of Hachette Children's Books,
an Hachette UK company.
www.hachette.co.uk

How to be a hero

This book is not like others you may have read. You are the hero of this adventure. It is up to you to make decisions that will affect how the adventure unfolds.

Each section of this book is numbered. At the end of most sections, you will have to make a choice. The choice you make will take you to a different section of the book.

Some of your choices will help you to complete the adventure successfully. But choose carefully, some of your decisions could be fatal!

If you fail, then start the adventure again and learn from your mistake.

If you choose correctly you will succeed in your mission.

Don't be a zero, be a hero!

You are a skilled warrior, living in a world of enchantment and danger. Humans live alongside trolls, elves and dwarves, while other mysterious creatures walk in the shadows.

You were once a member of the City Guards of Alba — a league of the greatest, bravest warriors. However, twenty moons ago you fought with your captain. He was bullying young recruits and you felt he needed to be taught a lesson. You won the fight, but your captain was mortally wounded. You were brought before the Queen of Alba. She sent you into exile, banning you from ever returning to the city. Since that day you have drifted from town to town, finding work where you can.

Your latest home is the busy sea port of Krassa, where you are working alongside a blacksmith at a forge, making swords and tools. It is hard work — something that has never worried you — but you know that this is no job for someone with your skills. You hope that your luck will change...

Go to section 1.

1

It is a warm spring morning and the work is hot. Sweat drips from your brow. As you hammer at a piece of red-hot metal, a man arrives at the forge. He is dressed in the uniform of the City Guards of Alba and calls you by your name — he knows who you are!

Your hand tightens around the forge hammer. "Who asks for me?" you say.

"I am Olderon," he replies. "I have been searching for you for many days."

"For what purpose?" you ask.

"To take you back to Alba. The queen needs your help..."

You stare at the man. "The queen banished me. Why would she seek my help now?"

"Come back to Alba and find out," he says.

You wonder if the man is trying to trick you. "How do I know what you say is true?"

"I give you my word as a City Guard of Alba," he replies.

"I knew a captain of the city guards," you reply. "I had no trust in him."

"If you do not trust my word, then I appeal to your honour. Our city is in great danger. You are our last chance..."

If you wish to return to Alba with Olderon, go to 25.

If you do not trust Olderon, go to 38.

2

You shake your head. "I cannot accept this quest. It is far too dangerous."

"You are a coward!" says the queen. "Your banishment continues for the rest of your life. If you are ever seen in Alba, you will be killed. Now go!"

You head out of the palace, destined to walk the world forever known as a coward.

You are no hero! Begin your adventure again. Go to 1.

3

You look at the Spellcaster's bloody wound and realise that the ghoul's blood has infected him. If he is not killed then he will become a ghoul.

"I will do as you ask," you say. The old man closes his eyes and you carry out his last wish.

You and Olderon take the astrolabe and head out of the city to the spot where you left Hergal. You find the gryphon patiently awaiting your return. The astrolabe points to the south and soon you are flying over the desert towards the Lost Temple.

The gryphon speeds through the air, but ahead you can see that the sky is getting darker. The wind beats at you and grains of sand sting your face.

"A sandstorm!" says Olderon. "What should we do?"

If you wish to turn back and find shelter, go to 24.

If you wish to continue to fly onwards, go to 39.

4

You return to Alba and inform the queen of the attack. Hergal is made ready for your journey, and soon you and Olderon are flying on the gryphon towards Barrsa.

The journey takes some hours, but there is no sign of the vampire bats. Eventually you see the port with its great sandstone walls.

"Where should we land, inside the city or outside the walls?" asks Olderon.

If you wish to land inside the city of Barrsa, go to 45.

To land outside Barrsa, go to 27.

5

"I'm sorry," you say. You close your eyes and let go of Olderon's wrist. He makes no sound as he falls through the air.

You lie on the rocky path for some time. You know that you cannot go back to Alba — you will be branded a coward for letting Olderon die.

You are destined to live in exile, forever.

You let Olderon fall to his death. You are no hero! Start again — go to 1.

6

You draw your sword and charge at the wraiths. But you are too slow. One of the creatures plunges its sword into Olderon's body. He drops down dead.

You give a cry of horror and the wraiths take their opportunity. Two of the creatures fly at you and rip the amulet from your grasp. Without the Ruby of Power to help, you know that you are in trouble.

You slash at your enemies with your sword.

Go to 40.

7

"Who is this Red Queen?" you ask.

The queen waves her hand and an image appears. "She lives on the far side of the world in Necropolis: the City of the Dead," she says. "Her husband is the necromancer Mortha. He was once a great spellcaster, but sought greater powers. He wishes to rule the world with his queen and has been searching for the

rubies from the Blood Crown.

"It seems that they have already found the Ruby of Death. With it, they have raised an army of the dead. If they find the other rubies, then nothing will be able to stop them."

If you have not found out about the rubies, go to 41.

If you already know about the rubies, go to 23.

8

Some time later you wake up. The sun beats down on your broken body. You try to look around, but you can't move your head.

You cry out for help, but there is no one to save you.

You lie helpless in the sand, knowing that you are doomed to rest here forever.

You have failed. To begin again, go to 1.

9

"We seek the Spellcaster of the city," you say. "We hope he can help us in our quest."

In reply, the black-robed men draw their swords and point them at you.

"We have been waiting for you," replies one of the men. "Our mistress, the Red Queen, told us you were on the way..."

If you want to fight the guards, go to 22.
If you wish to talk to them, go to 30.

10

"I will not go back," you snarl and swing the hammer at Olderon.

He avoids you and reaches for his sword. He lunges at you and pain slices through your body as the blade pierces your side.

You fall to your knees, blood pouring from the wound.

Olderon stands over you. "You have no honour — and now you have no future." He turns away, leaving you bleeding in the dirt.

If you wish to begin the adventure again, go to 1.

11

"I agree," you say.

The captain spins the wheel and swings the ship about. You and Olderon rush to the ship's stern. You take up your bow and shoot at the swarm of bats. You hit several and soon the creatures turn back and disappear into the distance.

"A warning from the Red Queen," you say. "I'm sure they won't be the last of her servants to try to stop us."

"What should we do now?" asks Olderon.

"Return to Alba and fly to Barrsa on the gryphon. Our enemies know we are on our way, there is no point trying to conceal ourselves."

Go to 4.

12

"I do not know the answer," you say. "I need another clue."

In reply the sphinx lifts its great stone paw. It hovers above you for a second. By the time you realise what's happening, it's too late.

Tonnes of stone crash down on you and Olderon, crushing your bodies. Your blood seeps between the sphinx's toes and into the hot desert sand.

Try to remember clues as you go along. Start your adventure again — go to 1.

As the firebird screeches towards you, the
skeleton rider pulls back his arm and hurls
the spear at you.

You dodge the spear, but the distraction is
fatal. The firebird's razor-sharp talons tear
into your chest. You feel your ribs being ripped
apart. The creature grips you and wraps you
in its wings of flame. You scream in agony, but
soon pass out. The firebird releases you and
you hit the stone floor, dead.

**What a disaster! Begin your quest again —
go to 1.**

14

You and Olderon draw your swords as the men
head towards you. There is a clash of metal as
their blades meet yours.

You score some direct blows but there are
too many of them. Hergal knocks some down
with her talons, but more men appear from a
building nearby.

The attackers press forward and surround
Olderon. You hear his cries as the men's swords
find their mark and he drops to the floor, dead.

The attackers turn their attention to you.
You are fighting for your life!

Go to 40.

15

"We are just poor travellers seeking rest," you
answer.

"You are a liar!" snarls the captain. "We know
who you are and why you are here. We saw your
gryphon flying over the city and our mistress,
the Red Queen, has warned us about you!"

**If you wish to continue to talk to the
guards, go to 30.**

If you want to fight the guards, go to 22.

You know that you have to stop the troll's attack.

"Hold on!" you shout at Olderon. With one movement you reach for your bow and notch an arrow. You aim, pull back the bowstring and send the arrow flying into the troll's chest.

The troll drops the boulder and staggers, before plunging over the cliff. You leap from your horse and dive forward, grabbing Olderon's wrist just as he loses his grip on the rocky cliff face.

You grit your teeth and hang on. But his weight pulls you towards the edge of the cliff.

"Let me go," he says. "Save yourself..."

If you want to do as Olderon says, go to 5.

If you want to try to pull him back up, go to 48.

17

"We have to fight back," you tell Olderon, urging Hergal towards the genie.

You draw your sword. It is almost impossible to see anything through the stinging sand that tears at your body, but you can just make out the dark outline of the genie.

With one movement, you leap off the gryphon, hurtle through the air and plunge your sword into the genie's chest. Holding firmly onto the hilt, you slide down the monster's body, cutting open its chest. Sand pours from the gaping wound and the creature cries out in agony.

You hit the ground and leap out of the way as the genie's body crashes downwards.

A cloud of sand engulfs you and you close your eyes and cover your mouth.

The storm subsides and all that remains of your foe is a giant sand dune. Hergal lands and Olderon hauls you back onto the gryphon. "Well fought! Now let's find this lost temple!"

Go to 26.

18

"There is no point trying to conceal our journey," you say. "The Red Queen knows that we seek the rubies. It will be quicker to fly."

"Very well," says the queen. "May good fortune be with you."

Soon you and Olderon are flying on the gryphon over the sea towards Barrsa.

The gryphon's great wings cut through the air and hours later you see land ahead. You point out the port of Barrsa with its sandstone walls with watchtowers.

"Where should we land, inside the city or outside the walls?" asks Olderon.

If you wish to land inside the city, go to 45.

If you would rather land outside the city, go to 27.

You and Olderon put away your swords and sit down on the carpet.

The woman stares at you and a strange smile breaks across her face. A feeling of unease passes through your body.

"How did you know we were coming?" you ask the woman.

"My mistress told me!" she says and throws a yellow powder onto an oil lamp. There is an explosion and the room is filled with fire and smoke.

Olderon's clothes burst into flames and he cries out in agony.

As you are engulfed by the flames, you hear the sound of maniacal laughter. Peering through the fire you see the old woman for what she really is — a ghoul!

It is the last thing you see as the monstrous creature moves towards you, mouth wide open, revealing sharp deadly teeth that will feed on your cooked flesh.

You have failed to find the Ruby of Power. To begin your quest again, go to 1.

"I will tell you of the legend of the Blood Crown," says the queen. "Back in the mists of time, Solmor, the world's greatest Spellcaster created the Crown of Rubies for the High King.

"This magnificent crown was made of pure gold, and the rubies set into it were no ordinary gemstones — each held a special power. Together, they helped to create the most powerful object in the world, giving the High King control over others.

"But rulers across our world became greedy for this power. The High King was the first to die in battle as he fought for the crown against rival lords. Many more bloody wars were fought over the crown, and so it was renamed the Blood Crown."

"I have heard of this story," you say. "But doesn't the legend say that the crown was broken up?"

The queen nods. "Indeed. Realising that the Blood Crown was a force for evil, just before his death, Solmor broke it up and had the rubies hidden across the world. We have asked you here because—"

Before the queen can finish, there is a huge crash as the doors to the great hall burst open and a giant flaming bird flies inside. On its back sits a skeleton, holding a silver spear. The firebird swoops towards the queen.

You have to act immediately!

To attack with your bow, go to 28.
To attack with your sword, go to 36.

"We have to trust the astrolabe," you tell Olderon. "But just in case something happens to me, you stay here."

Holding the astrolabe, you take a deep breath and step into the flaming lake. The flames immediately die down and you wade safely through the oil to reach the island.

You enter the golden dome. A staircase leads down into its depths. Holding your sword, you carefully make your way down the stairs and into a dark, vaulted room.

"I was expecting someone," a voice says. A torch bursts into flames, and standing before you is an old bearded man. He is holding a bow. The arrow is pointing at your chest! Around his neck is a golden amulet. In the middle sits a large red ruby.

"Yes, it is the Ruby of Power," he says, as if reading your mind. "And you will not take it!" He draws back the bowstring.

If you wish to attack the man, go to 37.
If you want to talk to the old man, go to 43.

You and Olderon draw your swords and begin your attack.

You strike at a guard and your blade pierces his body. To your amazement the guard turns into a giant cobra. The creature spits deadly poison at you, which you just manage to avoid. With lightning speed, you spin around and chop off the cobra's head.

You and Olderon continue the battle, but the other guards also turn into snakes when they are hit. "I'll strike the guards, you take care of the snakes," you tell Olderon.

Olderon's swords swings, chopping off the heads of more snakes, until they litter the ground. You hack into the soft snake bodies until they stop thrashing around. Soon the snake guards are all dead. You lean on your sword and turn to Olderon. "The Red Queen knew of our plans," you say. "We must be careful."

You pass through the gate and head into the city to find the Spellcaster.

Go to 35.

The queen continues her story. "Fortunately, Solmor realised that the power of the Blood Crown may again be needed to fight evil. He had this message carved onto a golden tablet." She signals a councillor to show you the tablet.

To the one who seeks the Blood Crown in a worthy cause, I leave this instruction. To find the Ruby of Power, seek the Blind Man of the Lost Temple of the Desert. All the other rubies will follow...

"But what is this all to do with me?" you ask.

The queen answers, "We wish you to journey to the Lost Temple, find the Ruby of Power and then hunt down the others. With these we will be able to defeat the Red Queen."

You are surprised. "Why me?" you ask.

"We have already sent many city guards to find the rubies, but none have returned. You and Olderon are our last hope..."

If you wish to accept the quest, go to 46.
If you do not wish to, go to 2.

24

"We have to turn back," you cry as the clouds of sand head towards you at lightning speed.

You turn Hergal around and urge her to fly as fast as possible. But even the gryphon's speed is not enough to outrun the storm. A savage gust of wind sends Hergal spinning and you lose your grip on her reins. You plunge through the air and hit the ground with a bone-breaking crunch. Pain courses through your body and you pass out into blackness.

Go to 8.

25

"Very well, I will return to Alba," you say.

"You have chosen honourably," replies Olderon. "I have horses saddled and ready for us."

You say farewell to the forge master, pack your sword and bow, and set off. After a day of hard travelling you find yourselves heading up a mountain pass with a long drop to one side.

As you ride along the narrow path you hear

a great roar above you. You glance up to see a huge mountain troll standing on a ledge directly above you. The creature hurls a boulder at you. It crashes down onto the path causing Olderon's horse to rear up. The city guard is thrown over the side of the cliff but manages to grab hold of the rocky edge.

"Help me!" he cries.

There is another roar from above. You look up to see the troll getting ready to attack again.

If you want to try to rescue Olderon, go to 44.

If you wish to attack the troll, go to 16.

26

The astrolabe points your way across the desert. As the sun sets, the desert sands turn a blood-red colour. You hope this is not a bad omen.

You just make out the shape of a pyramid in the distance. To one side of it stands a sphinx carved in stone. The astrolabe points directly towards it. You land and stand before the great stone figure.

To your amazement, the sphinx opens its eyes and speaks! "Who are you and what do you seek?"

You tell the creature of your quest.

"If you wish to find the Lost Temple," it says, "you must answer the following riddle: If you give me food, I live. If you give me water, I die. What am I?"

If you think you know the answer, go to 33.
If you want more information, go to 12.

27

"We don't want people to be scared of us," you say. "We'll land outside the city and enter on foot."

"I agree," replies Olderon.

You guide Hergal to the sand dunes beyond the city walls. You leave the gryphon and head to the city gate.

There are several armed guards at the gate. The captain orders you to stop. "Who are you, strangers, and what do you want?" he asks.

If you want to tell the truth, go to 9.
If you want to hide the truth, go to 15.

With lightning speed you load your bow, aim and shoot at the firebird. The arrow strikes home. You shoot again and score another deadly hit.

The firebird plunges to the ground, sending its rider crashing to the floor. You draw your sword and attack the skeleton, slashing at its clattering white bones. It thrusts its spear towards you, but you spin away and cut through the creature's neck. The skeleton drops to the floor, turning into a cloud of dust.

Olderon slaps you on the back. "Well fought."

"What was that creature?" you ask. "And where did it come from?"

The queen replies, "It was sent by our enemy, the Red Queen and her husband, Mortha, the necromancer. They are searching for the rubies from the Blood Crown."

If you wish to know more about the rubies, go to 41.

If you wish to find out more about the Red Queen, go to 7.

You hold up the amulet. "I will surrender the amulet. Here it is. But you must first release Olderon."

"We will," replies the wraith. "We will release him from his life." The creature plunges his sword into Olderon's body. You give a cry as your companion drops to the floor.

The wraiths attack, but the ruby gives you great power. You move at incredible speed, slashing at the wraiths' rotting bodies and avoiding their blades.

The battle is soon over. The bodies of your enemies lie scattered on the temple floor. You hurry over to Olderon, who lies bleeding from the wraith's deadly blow.

Go to 50.

30

You hold up you hand. "We come in peace."

Before you can continue one of the men draws back his hand. There is a blur of movement and Olderon gives a cry. You stare at him and see a blade embedded in his chest. He drops to the ground, dead.

You draw your sword and ready yourself for a fight to the death.

Go to 40.

31

You shake your head. "I cannot do that."

"Then die!" The Spellcaster leaps up and attacks you — he has turned into a ghoul! He plunges his razor sharp teeth into your neck and you scream as the creature rips at your flesh.

Olderon reacts and kills your attacker with his sword.

You hold your hand to the gaping wound in your neck. You realise that the ghoul's blood had mixed with the Spellcaster's, turning him into a ghoul. You look at your blood stained hands. "If the Spellcaster turned into a ghoul then so will I..."

Olderon nods. "Then you too must die..."

You realise that Olderon is right. "Do what you have to," you say as you close your eyes and wait for your end.

You have failed in your quest. If you wish to begin again, go to 1.

32

"I have no time for stories," you say. "If there is a task to do, let me get on with it."

"You are too hasty," the queen replies. "Stories can tell us great truths and help to guide our actions."

You consider for a moment. The queen is right, you should take time to think before you act. You bow your head. "Forgive me. Please tell the story."

Go to 20.

You remember the Spellcaster's words. "The answer is fire," you reply. You feed it wood; it burns, if you pour on water; it dies out.

The sphinx nods. A grating noise cuts through the desert night and you see that a door into the pyramid has opened. "That which you seek is within," says the sphinx.

You and Olderon head into the pyramid. Flaming torches light up your way as you walk through the narrow stone passages.

Eventually you arrive at the opening to an underground lake of burning oil. In the centre of the lake is a golden-domed temple — the Lost Temple! The astrolabe points directly towards the dome. "We have to get to the dome," says Olderon. "But how?"

"The Spellcaster said we should trust the astrolabe," you reply.

Olderon looks surprised. "You think we should just walk across the lake?"

If you wish to walk towards the Lost Temple, go to 21.

If you want to look for another way across, go to 47.

34

"It would be better if people did not know we are in Barrsa," you say. "Let us go by sea."

"Very well," says the queen. "May good fortune be with you."

Some hours later you and Olderon are on board the ship, heading across the sea towards Barrsa.

"How long until we reach land?" you ask the captain.

"Another day if the wind holds good," he answers. "But you can never tell—" he breaks off and points ahead. A large black cloud has suddenly formed in the sky. "What is that?" he asks in wonder. The cloud heads towards you at unnatural speed...

Olderon gives a cry of alarm. "That isn't a cloud, it's a swarm of giant vampire bats!"

"We must turn back," says the captain.

If you think you should turn back, go to 11.

If you want to continue your journey by sea, go to 49.

35

You head to the marketplace and ask a trader for directions to the Spellcaster's home.

"You are the second person in the last hour to ask for directions to the old man's house," he replies.

This is worrying news. "We must hurry then."

You follow the trader's directions through the alleyways of Barrsa and arrive at a small sandstone house. The door is open. You draw your sword and enter.

Oil lamps light up the darkness and you can make out the figure of an old woman sitting on a carpet. "I was expecting you," she says. "I am the Spellcaster. Put away your weapons and sit down."

If you wish to do as she says, go to 19.

If you want to keep hold of your sword, go to 42.

36

You unsheathe your sword and run towards the creature. Jumping on a table, you fling yourself at the firebird. You swing your sword, but the great beast flies out of your reach and you find yourself thrashing at air.

Urged on by its skeleton rider, the firebird banks around and flies straight towards you.

If you want to continue to attack with your sword, go to 13.

If you wish to use your bow, go to 28.

37

You leap towards the old man, but are too slow. He shoots the arrow, which slams into your chest. You drop to the floor and try to crawl away.

Although he is blind, the power of the ruby gives him superhuman powers and he is able to shoot several more arrows into your body at incredible speed.

"I warned you that you would never take the ruby," he says.

These are the last words you hear as death takes hold of you.

You have failed your quest at the last hurdle! To begin again, go to 1.

38

You shake your head. "The queen banished me. I have no duty to anyone."

Olderon pulls out his sword. "Then you do not deserve to live. I give you one last chance. Come with me to Alba or face the consequences."

If you wish to fight Olderon, go to 10.

If you want to change your mind and go to Alba, go to 25.

39

"We go on," you say.

The clouds of sand hit, and you hang on tightly to Hergal as the gryphon flies through the raging storm. Sand fills the air and you can hardly breathe. As you are about to pass out, the storm suddenly dies away.

You wipe the sand from your eyes and peer ahead. Your blood turns cold as you stare at the huge cloud-like figure standing before you.

"A sand genie," says Olderon. "I have heard the legends of such creatures. They are very dangerous."

The creature opens its mouth and roars,
sending raging clouds of sand towards you.

If you want to turn back, go to 24.
If you want to fight the genie, go to 17.

40

You fight bravely, but there are too many enemies to overcome. Their weapons cut into your flesh as they press forward with their attack.

You feel a blade slice into your back. You turn, but more blades pierce your body. You drop to the ground, bleeding and helpless. You close your eyes as your foes move in for the final kill.

To begin again, go to 1.

41

"Tell me about these rubies," you say.

"There were four rubies," replies the queen. "Each had a different power. The Ruby of Power gives the owner great fighting skills. The Ruby of Seeing gives the gift of telepathy and reading minds. The Ruby of Magic gives the gift of great magical powers and the Ruby of Death gives its wearer the power over death."

"I can understand why someone would want such powerful gems," you say.

"Quite so," replies the queen. "And that is why the Red Queen seeks the rubies. To win power over all the peoples of the world."

If you know all about the Red Queen, go to 23.

If you have not yet found out about the Red Queen, go to 7.

42

"I was told that the Spellcaster is a man, not a woman," you reply. "Show your real self!"

The room is filled with screeching as the woman leaps up at you. Her mouth opens revealing her razor-sharp teeth — she is a ghoul!

Your sword flashes in the light as you plunge it into the creature's body. The ghoul gives one last high-pitched shriek and decomposes before your eyes.

You hear a noise from an adjoining room. You hurry through to find an old man lying on the floor. He is bleeding from a deep wound to his neck. The ghoul's work, you think and help him to sit.

"You are the Spellcaster?" you ask.

The man nods and you tell him of your quest to seek out the Blind Man of the Lost Temple of the Desert.

In answer, he reaches into his pocket and pulls out a small, circular device. "This is an astrolabe. It will guide you to the Lost Temple if you trust it." He hands it to you. "You must also remember that 'fire' is the answer."

Before you can ask what he means, the Spellcaster speaks again. "The ghoul's touch has cursed me — you must stop me turning..."

To do as the Spellcaster asks, go to 3.

If you want to try to save the Spellcaster, go to 31.

"I do not wish to take the ruby from you," you say. "If you listen to my story, you will surely give it to me."

The old man lowers his bow. You stare at his sightless eyes and tell him the story of your quest. When you have finished, the old man takes off the amulet. "I am glad to pass on the burden. This ruby has kept me alive for many years and now it is time to let go."

"Do you know where the next ruby can be found?" you ask.

"The Ruby of Seeing is to be found in the mountains of the north. You must seek out the Dragon Princess. She is the ruby's guardian." He passes the amulet to you. You immediately feel stronger and more powerful. At the same moment, the old man drops to the floor. "My time has come. You must go..." He closes his eyes just as his body turns to ash.

You head out of the dome and cross the lake. You cannot see Olderon, so you call out his name.

He steps from the shadows of a pillar. Behind him stand half a dozen black-robed figures.

Their flesh is rotting and hangs from their skeletal figures. They are armed with swords and spears.

"They are death wraiths," explains Olderon. "They've been following us from the beginning of our journey."

One of the creatures holds a sword to Olderon's throat. "Save your friend," it rasps. "Surrender the ruby..."

If you want to negotiate with the wraiths, go to 29.

If you want to attack the death wraiths, go to 6.

44

You leap off your horse and run towards Olderon. Just as he loses his grip, you grab hold of Olderon's wrist and save him from plunging to his death.

However, your sense of relief is short lived. The troll hurls another huge boulder downwards. The huge rock smashes onto your back, shattering your bones and sending you and Olderon over the cliff edge to your deaths far below.

You are dead! Begin your adventure again — go to 1.

45

"It will be quicker to land inside the city," you reply.

Market traders cry out in astonishment as you guide Hergal downwards to land in a large square full of stalls.

As you dismount the gryphon, a dozen black-robed men appear, running towards you armed with lethal-looking curved swords.

To attack them, go to 14.
If you wish to talk to them, go to 30.

46

"I accept this quest and I am happy to share it with Olderon."

The queen smiles. "Then you must head to the Kingdom of the Sands. Go to the port of Barrsa and find the Spellcaster of the city. He may be able to help you to discover the Blind Man of the Lost Temple."

"Barrsa is many miles away, how will we get there?" you ask.

The queen signals to a servant, who opens a large set of doors. You gasp in amazement as a gryphon is led into the hall!

"Her name is Hergal," says Olderon. "She will fly us to Barrsa. But if you do not care for flying, we can sail. There is a ship waiting for us in the harbour. Flying would be quicker but our arrival on a gryphon would attract attention to our task. How do you wish to travel?"

If you wish to fly to Barrsa, go to 18.
If you wish to sail to Barrsa, go to 34.

47

You point at the boat floating on the lake. "That's the way across."

Olderon is not so sure. "The astrolabe is pointing to the dome, not the boat."

"You stay here then," you say. You get into the boat and cast off. You begin to row across the lake. Suddenly there is a great roaring noise and the flames around you flare up, engulfing the boat.

With a cry you leap from the boat and just manage to reach the shore. Olderon throws his cloak on you, beats at the flames and puts them out.

You lie on the ground, breathing deeply. "I owe you my life," you say.

"I have repaid my debt to you," he replies. "We are even."

Go to 21.

48

"Never!" you say. Summoning all your strength, you move backwards, pulling Olderon upwards to safety.

With one last surge, you pull him onto the path.

You both lie on the ground breathing heavily. "I owe you my life," says Olderon.

"You are a city guard, it was my duty," you reply. "Now let us head back to Alba."

It takes two days of riding to reach Alba. Olderon takes you to the great hall in the queen's palace. The queen and her councillors are waiting for you. You bow.

"It is many moons since you last stood before me," says the queen.

"And you unfairly banished me," you say.

"Silence!" demands one of the councillors.

The queen raises a hand. "No, it is good that you have passion. I have a great quest for you."

"What is this quest?" you ask.

"All will be revealed in good time," replies the queen. "But I wish to tell you an old story..."

If you wish to know what your quest is, go to 32.

If you wish to listen to the story, go to 20.

49

"We go on," you tell the captain.

He throws his hands in the air. "This is madness!"

Minutes later the cloud of giant vampire bats hits the ship. The air is a whirlwind of wings and snapping jaws as the creatures attack. Sailors drop to the deck, their lifeblood sucked from them.

You take up your bow and shoot at the giant bats. But there are too many of them. You watch helplessly as Olderon is smothered by the creatures. You hear his cries as his body is ripped to pieces.

Then the swarm turns towards you. The bats swarm about you, tearing at your flesh with their razor-sharp teeth and sucking on your blood. You sink to the floor and pass into oblivion.

You've been drained of your lifeblood! To begin again, go to 1.

50

You realise that Olderon's wound is fatal — you can do nothing for him.

"I am not long for this world," he says. "Did you find the Blind Man?"

You nod and tell him what happened in the temple.

"Then you must take Hergal, fly to the North and find the Dragon Princess. You have to succeed or the Red Queen will triumph."

With that, Olderon closes his eyes and submits to death.

At that moment the temple begins to shake. Pillars collapse and huge stones fall from the roof. The pyramid is falling down! You have to get out! Leaving the body of your companion, you race through the passages as the pyramid collapses around you.

You emerge into the cool desert night where Hergal is waiting.

Soon you are flying across the desert sands, the wind rushing through your hair.

You succeeded! You have the Ruby of Power around your neck, and the Blood Crown cannot be remade without it. But Olderon — your brave friend — is gone. You try not to linger on those thoughts.

Now you are heading for the mountains of the north to find the Dragon Princess and the Ruby of Seeing.

You know there will be tougher battles ahead...

You must prevent the Red Queen from taking over the world...

1

You fly towards the jagged peaks of the northern mountains on your gryphon, Hergal.

After many hours of flying, you see the small village of Drakensberg, one of the few places to be found in this harsh landscape. You are sure the Dragon Princess will be somewhere nearby.

How you will approach the village of Drakensberg?

If you want to fly over the village and land in the square, go to 16.

If you wish to land unseen, go to 31.

Continue the adventure in:

BLOOD CROWN QUEST 2

DRAGON MOUNTAIN

About the 2Steves

"The 2Steves" are
Britain's most popular
writing double act
for young people,
specialising in comedy
and adventure. They
perform regularly in schools and libraries,
and at festivals, taking the power of words
and story to audiences of all ages.

Together they have written many books,
including the *Crime Team* and *iHorror* series.

About the illustrator: Jack Lawrence

Jack Lawrence is a successful freelance
comics illustrator, working on titles such as
A.T.O.M., Cartoon Network, *Doctor Who
Adventures*, *2000 AD*, *Gogos Mega Metropolis*
and *Spider-Man Tower of Power*. He also works
as a freelance toy designer.

Jack lives in Maidstone in Kent with
his partner and two cats.

Want to read more "You Are The Hero" adventures? Well, why not try these...

978 0 7496 9283 4 pb
978 1 4451 0843 8 eBook

A millionaire is found at his luxury island home – dead! But no one can work out how he died. You must get to Skull Island and solve the mystery before his killer escapes.

978 0 7496 9284 1 pb
978 1 4451 0844 5 eBook

The daughter of a Hong Kong businessman has been kidnapped. You must find her, but who took her and why? You must crack the case, before it's too late!

978 0 7496 9286 5 pb
978 1 4451 0845 2 eBook

You must solve the clues to stop a terrorist attack in London. But who is planning the attack, and when will it take place? It's a race against time!

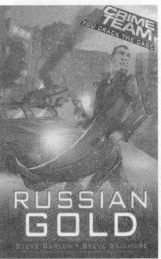

978 0 7496 9285 8 pb
978 1 4451 0846 9 eBook

An armoured convoy has been attacked in Moscow and hundreds of gold bars stolen. But who was behind the raid, and where is the gold? Get the clues — get the gold.

Also by the 2Steves: iHorror

Fight your fear. Choose your fate.

978 1 40830 985 8 pb
978 1 40831 476 0 eBook

978 1 40830 986 5 pb
978 1 40831 477 7 eBook

978 1 40830 988 9 pb
978 1 40831 479 1 eBook

978 1 40830 987 2 pb
978 1 40831 478 4 eBook

www.orchardbooks.co.uk